I See

Teacher's
Choice
Series

Shirley Frederick
Rapid City, South Dakota

Illustrations by
Rick Faust

Dominie Press, Inc.

The development of the *Teacher's Choice Series* was supported by the Reading Recovery project at California State University, San Bernardino. All authors' royalties from the sale of the *Teacher's Choice Series* will be used to support various Reading Recovery projects.

Publisher: Raymond Yuen
Series Editor: Stanley L. Swartz
Illustrator: Rick Faust
Cover Designer: Steve Morris
Page Design: Pamela S. Pettigrew

Published by:

ᴇ Dominie Press, Inc.

1949 Kellogg Avenue
Carlsbad, California 92008 USA

ISBN 1-56270-542-3
Printed in Singapore by PH Productions.
2 3 4 5 6 PH 99 98 97

I see an eagle.

I see a hawk.

I see two deer.

I see some prairie dogs.

I see a coyote.

I see a buffalo.

The buffalo sees me!

About the Author

Shirley Frederick graduated from the University of New Hampshire in 1958 and received a M.Ed. from the Harvard Graduate School of Education in 1959. She has studied ecology at the Black Hills Natural Sciences Field Station, The Yellowstone Institute, and the Teton Science School. She has taught in elementary schools since 1959 and is presently a Reading Recovery™ teacher for the Rapid City Area Schools in South Dakota. In her writing, Shirley draws on themes that are familiar to Native American children.